A first book of letters

Top and Toby

Written by David Lloyd
Illustrated by Charlotte Voake

PUBLISHED BY THE READER'S DIGEST ASSOCIATION LIMITED

One fine day
Top and his dog Toby
set out to have an
adventure.

They decided to explore
the letters
of the alphabet.

a

After a long walk
they arrived at a.

An artist lived there
all alone.

a

b

b was broken
so Top built it up again
while Toby begged for
biscuits.

b

C

C was curved
and covered with crows.

Top climbed it.

Toby chased the crows.

C

d

Together
Top and Toby
did a dance on d.

d

e

They tried to eat e,
which wasn't easy.

e

f

They made faces at f,
just for fun.

f

g

They grew gardens
on g.

g

h

h made them happy
so they hugged it.

h

i

"I spy ice-cream,"
Top said, when
they reached **i**.

i

j

j seemed just the place
to jump from.

j

k

They kissed k.

k

1

They licked 1
like a lollipop.

m

They measured m
most carefully.

m

n

n looked nice to nibble.

n

O

They opened **O**
and found oranges
inside.

O

p

They painted p pink.

p

q

When they reached q,
they bowed quietly
to the queen.

q

r

They ran races round r.

r

S

S looked like a snake.

"Stay away," Top said
to Toby, "snakes sting."

S

t

Toby tickled t
with his tail.

"Tee hee," said Top.

t

u

They undid all u's
buttons.

U was upset.

u

V

They pretended V
was a violent volcano.

V

W

They filled **W** with
water and washed in it.

W

X

They did exercises on X
until they were
exhausted.

X

y

Top yelled at y,
but Toby just yawned
and yawned.

y

Z

By the time they
reached **Z** they were
both very tired.

So they made up some
beds and went to sleep.
Zzzzz.

Z

In their sleep
Top and Toby dreamed
that they took all the
letters to visit the artist
living alone in a.

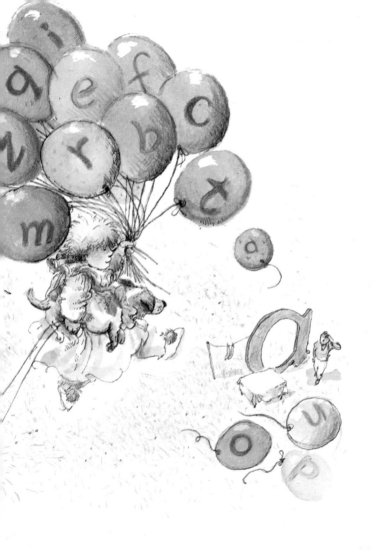

They had a party,

the greatest, wildest,

happiest party ever.

MY FIRST LIBRARY

First Edition Copyright © 1980
The Reader's Digest Association Limited,
Berkeley Square House, Berkeley Square,
London W1X 6AB
Reprinted 1990

Copyright © 1980
The Reader's Digest Association
Far East Limited

® READER'S DIGEST, THE DIGEST and
the Pegasus logo are registered trademarks of
The Reader's Digest Association, Inc.
of Pleasantville, New York, U.S.A.

Printed in Hong Kong